INTRODUCTION

An increasing number of teachers of mathematics at all levels are including in their work, opportunities for children to explore and investigate potentially mathematical situations. Six sessions at the A.T.M. Conference at Nottingham in 1977 were devoted to work of this kind. These attracted considerable interest, but one difficulty expressed by many teachers was that of finding sources or examples of suitable starting points for investigations. This pamphlet is the first of a series: it is intended to provide situations for investigation which teachers have found useful with children of varying age and ability.

The investigations included in this first pamphlet draw on the experience of many teachers. None are original. We have included examples which cover a wide range of types and levels of difficulty, and we have attempted to indicate this on the following page. Categorisation of investigations in this way is inevitably subjective, but it may be helpful for those who have not used material of this sort before.

A second pamphlet is in preparation, and we rely on you to send to the A.T.M. office any starting points you have found useful at any level, from infant to sixth form.

TANSY HARDY   ANNE HAWORTH   ERIC LOVE   ALISTAIR McINTOSH

SOME CATEGORIES

- Patterns in Number

    Number chains 17, 29, 39, 64, 65

    Numbers from geometrical configurations 1, 4, 6, 14, 18, 21, 26, 43, 44, 52, 53, 57, 59, 61

    Partitions 2, 7, 10, 30, 51, 54, 55

    Sets of numbers that are constrained 5, 11, 12, 19, 22, 34, 35, 37, 48, 56, 58, 60, 69, 71

- Spatial

    Dissections and Replications 9, 27, 32, 45, 46, 72

    Combinatorial arrangements 38, 43, 47, 68, 70

    Constrained arrangements 8, 9, 16, 20, 21, 31, 33, 36, 42, 45, 50, 62, 67, 73

- Symbolisation 3, 18, 23, 25, 40, 49, 66, 74

- Games and Puzzles 13, 21, 24, 41, 52, 63

- Structure 15, 28, 44

- Suitable for younger children 5, 15, 18, 26, 37, 53, 55, 58, 59, 73, 75

- Mainly for 14+ or sixth form 2, 3, 7, 8, 9, 11, 16, 19, 24, 25, 27, 28, 31, 32, 33, 26, 42, 45, 48, 63, 64, 65, 69, 70, 71, 72, 74

LIST OF STARTING POINTS

1. ROUTES

a) Start at A and travel along lines only in these two directions → and ↑. In how many different ways can you get from A to each of the lettered points?

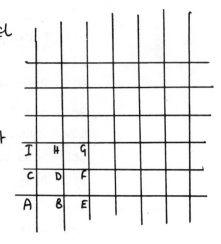

Try other points. Can you spot some patterns? Can you generalise them? Can you explain or prove them?

b) Start at A and move in any of these directions:

Investigate as before.

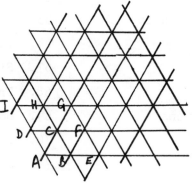

c) Invent your own grids and rules for moves.

2. NUMBER PAIRS

Choose any number, eg 21.
Form a number pair by taking 21 mod 2, which is 1, and 21 mod 3, which is 0.
So 21 → (1,0). Also 17 → (1,2).

Find all possible such pairs.
Investigate what happens to the pairs when you add, subtract, multiply or divide the original numbers.

Extend this to number triples, etc.

3. RAILS

A child has a large number of curved rails in a train set. They are all quarter circles, and can be placed either left ↖ or right ↗.

Investigate the ways to make closed tracks.

4. DOTS AND LINES

Mark six dots on a sheet of plain paper

How many straight lines are needed to join each dot to every other dot?

Try for other arrangements of six dots.

What is the maximum number of lines which might be needed with only six dots?

Are there any number of lines smaller than the maximum that are not possible?

5. MULTIPLICATION SQUARE

Make a ten-by-ten multiplication square. Investigate number patterns on it.

6. LINES AND SQUARES

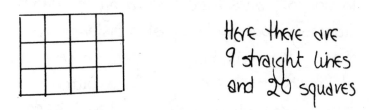

Here there are 10 straight lines and 17 squares.

Here there are 9 straight lines and 20 squares

Find the smallest number of lines needed to make exactly 100 squares

Investigate further.

How many different ways can you make a particular number of squares?

7. KEEP MOVING!

Drivers of cars are urged to keep a 'safe' distance behind the car in front. But what is safe?

In Holland, drivers are advised by the Dutch Highway Code to 'keep at a distance in metres which is half the speed (in km/hour) at which you are driving.' So a Dutch driver going at 60 km/hour should keep 30 metres behind the car in front of him.

On a new busy city ring road in Holland, the intention is that as many cars as possible should use the road simultaneously. That is, that each minute as many cars as possible should be able to pass a particular point. Taking account of the Dutch Highway code advice, and assuming that the average car length is 4 metres, how fast should the cars travel?

8. DOTTY SQUARES AND TRIANGLES

Squares: Choose two points on a square lattice. When can they be adjacent corners of a square?
Opposite corners?

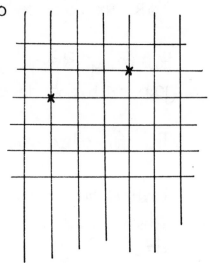

Triangles: On a triangular lattice, when can the two chosen points be corners of an equilateral triangle?

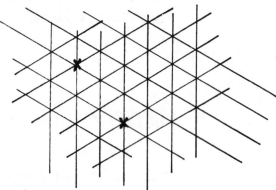

Investigate the areas of triangles and squares that you can make.
What about triangles on a square grid....?

9. FAULT LINES

Here is a rectangle made with some dominoes

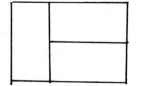

Each domino is a 2×1 rectangle.

A fault line is a straight line joining opposite sides of the rectangle. So this rectangle has a fault line here

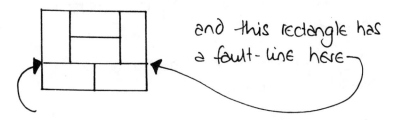

and this rectangle has a fault-line here

What is the smallest fault-free rectangle that you can find?

What is the smallest fault-free square?

Suppose you use 3×1 rectangles instead of dominoes?

10. SWEETS

When a boy counted his sweets in piles of four, he had two left over. When he counted them in piles of five, he had one left over. How many sweets could he have had?

Investigate other situations of this type.

11. BI-FRACTIONS

In binary,

0.1 represents $\frac{1}{2}$

0.01 represents $\frac{1}{4}$

and so on.

Investigate how other fractions can be written in binary.

$\frac{1}{3}$ is written as $0.\dot{0}\dot{1}$.

Can you explain why?

12. DISCS

a)

(6) (7) (8)

Here are three circular cardboard discs.
A number is written on the top of each disc.
There is also a number (not necessarily the same) written on the reverse side of each disc.

Throwing the discs in the air, and then adding the numbers on the faces, I have produced the following eight totals :

15, 16, 17,   19, 20, 21, 22, 23.

Can you work out what numbers are written on the reverse side of each disc?

b) Investigate totals produced by discs numbered differently. Can you produce eight consecutive numbers as totals?

Investigate for 2 discs

Are there ways of numbering 3 discs so each combination gives a different total?

13. TRIHEX

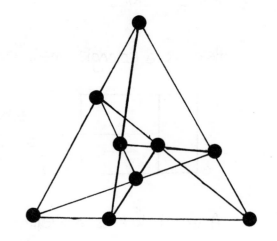

There are 9 cells on this board, joined by lines. Each player has 5 counters (one player has red, the other blue).
They take it in turns to put a counter in a cell.
The first player to have 3 counters in a straight line wins.

Investigate this game.

14. WATCH OUT

Imagine a city whose streets form a square grid, the sides of each square being 100 metres long, like this.
New York City on Manhattan Island is rather like this.

STREET
STREET

block of buildings.

Suppose that a policeman is standing at a street corner and that he can spot a suspicious person at 100m. So he can survey a maximum of 400m of street length, like this.

If we have a single block, with 4 corners, we need 2 policemen:
Two blocks in a row will need 3 policemen:

How many policemen are needed for 3 blocks?
4 blocks? 5 blocks?
What about blocks in squares? In rectangles?
Investigate further and see if you can find some rules

15. DOMINOES

Dominoes are put together in the usual way. Investigate the possibility of forming closed chains.

16. MATRICES

for the 2 by 2 matrix $\begin{pmatrix} 1 & 1 \\ -2 & 4 \end{pmatrix}$ we find that

$$\begin{pmatrix} 1 & 1 \\ -2 & 4 \end{pmatrix}\begin{pmatrix} 1 \\ 2 \end{pmatrix} = \begin{pmatrix} 3 \\ 6 \end{pmatrix} = 3\begin{pmatrix} 1 \\ 2 \end{pmatrix}$$

ie the vector $\begin{pmatrix} 1 \\ 2 \end{pmatrix}$ is transformed into a multiple of itself. Such vectors are called eigen vectors of the matrix.

Investigate eigenvectors.

17. BRACELETS

Start with any two numbers less than 10 —
say 1 and 5
Make a bracelet of numbers like this:

$$1 \rightarrow 5 \rightarrow 6 \rightarrow 1 \rightarrow 7 \rightarrow 8 \rightarrow 5 \rightarrow$$

Can you see how the chain is made?
Continue the chain — what happens?

Choose some more starting numbers and
investigate what happens.

How many different chains can you make?

What happens if you use numbers in
other bases?

18. TOWER OF HANOI

Discs are placed in
order, smallest on
top, on one peg.
You can move the
discs according to
these rules:

1. Move one disc at a time.
2. Do not put a bigger disc on a smaller one.

The object is to transfer all the discs to
another peg. Investigate for different numbers
of discs and pegs.

19. MONO DIVISORS

12 has 4 numbers less than itself with
only a factor of 1 in common with 12
(they are 11, 7, 5, 1) These are called the
monodivisors of 12. 6 has 2 monodivisors,
5 and 1. Investigate how many monodivisors
other numbers have.

20. SKELETONS

Imagine a square 'shrinking' uniformly

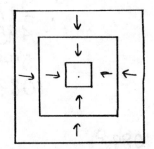

or a rectangle:

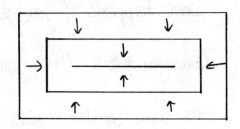

Both these figures have a 'skeleton' shown by the dotted lines in the diagrams opposite.

It's as though a densely packed army of ants starts on the edges of the shape and marches inwards at right angles to the edge at a constant speed. When one ant meets another, they stop. The skeleton

shows where the ants stop.

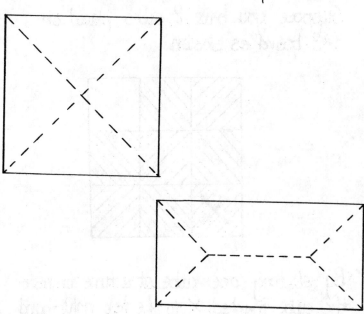

Investigate skeletons.

21. CUBE MOVES

Suppose you have 8 cubes placed on a 3×3 board as shown

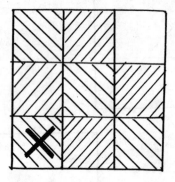

By sliding one cube at a time transfer the cube marked X to the top right-hand corner. How many moves are required?

Which is the best (shortest) route?

How many moves do you need if you are allowed to move more than one cube at a time.

Investigate for boards of different sizes? Any rules?

22. 1089

Write down a 3-digit number, say   742
Reverse the digits   247
Subtract   495
Reverse the digits   594
Add   1089

Do you always get 1089?

What happens if you start with 564?

Can you prove that you will always get 1089?

Are there similar results with 2 digits?
4 digits?

Extend to other bases.

23. KNIGHT'S MOVES

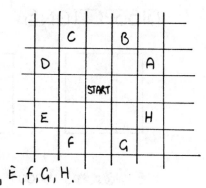

on a chessboard a
knight starting from
the marked square
can get to any of
the squares A, B, C, D, E, F, G, H.

If a is the move that gets to square A, b
the one that gets to square B, etc, then it
is possible to label each square as a sequence
of moves.

The same square can be reached in different
ways, both needing the same number of moves;
dgb and afc are the same square.

Investigate ways of finding equivalent labels
for the same square.

24. COIN GAME

One player puts down a 1p, a 2p and a 5p
coin on the table in any pattern of heads
and tails except all heads or all tails.
The coins are kept hidden.

The other player has to give instructions without
seeing the coins so that they will end up
all heads or all tails. An instruction will be,
for example, "reverse the 1p". After each
instruction the first player must say whether
or not the coins are all heads or all tails.

Investigate strategies.

25. FOLDS

fold a piece of paper in half, then in half again,
then open out

Investigate the shapes produced
and the patterns of right and left turns.

26. CHESSBOARD

How many squares here?
Five! where are they?

How many squares on a 3×3 board?
on a 4×4 board?

So how many squares on a chessboard?

What about other rectangular boards? e.g.

How many squares here?

Can you generalise your results?
How many squares on a m×m board?
on a m×n board?

How many rectangles on any of the boards?

27. DISSECTIONS

The diagrams show dissections of a 3×3 square
into rectangles.
The rules are (1) in each dissection the
rectangles are all different.
(2) the edges are all integers.

Investigate.

28. BINARY ORDER

The first 8 binary numbers may be arranged in
order so that only 1 digit is changed at a time,
and the last one can be changed back to the
first in the same way. One order is:-
000 → 001 → 011 → 010 → 111 → 101 → 100

Find all such orders and investigate relations between
them.

29. PARTITIONS

You could use Cuisenaire rods to help with this problem

The 3-rod can be partitioned (split up) in four different ways:

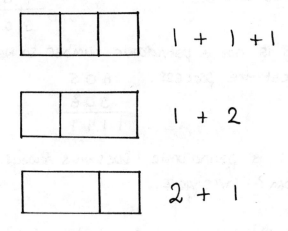

1 + 1 + 1

1 + 2

2 + 1

3

Investigate partitions of different numbers.

30. PRIMES

Fermat discovered that exactly half the prime numbers are the sum of two squares

eg: $29 = 25 + 4 = 5^2 + 2^2$

Make a list of the primes that you can form in this way, and a list of those that you can't form like this.

Try to find a rule which tests whether or not a prime can be made like this.

31. CUBE NETS

This diagram shows one possible net for an open cube.

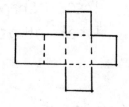

How many different cube nets can you find?

What about nets for other solids?

32. REPTILES

Squares can be fitted together to make larger similar shapes:

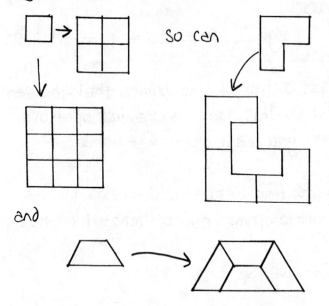

so can

These shapes are called reptiles. What others can you find?

33. GRAPHS

What lines go through the point (2,4) ?

34. PALINDROMES

a) Choose any number, reverse the digits, and add:

$$\begin{array}{r} 2\ 1\ 6 \\ 6\ 1\ 2 \\ \hline 8\ 2\ 8 \end{array}$$

828 is a palindromic number (the same backwards as forwards)

Try another number, reverse and add:

$$\begin{array}{r} 1\ 5\ 4 \\ 4\ 5\ 1 \\ \hline 6\ 0\ 5 \end{array}$$

605 is not a palindromic number, so we repeat the process:

$$\begin{array}{r} 6\ 0\ 5 \\ 5\ 0\ 6 \\ \hline 1\ 1\ 1\ 1 \end{array}$$

1111 is palindromic. Does this always happen? Investigate.

b) Are palindromic numbers multiples of 11?

c) The palindromic number 828 is the sum of 216 and its reverse 612. Take some palindromic numbers. Can you always make them by adding a number and its reverse? When you can, are there rules to find the numbers?

35. SUBTRACTION PATTERNS

This is a subtraction pattern:

```
5    11    8    15
   6     3    7    10
   3    4    3    4
     1    1    1    1
       0    0    0    0
```

it starts with the four numbers

```
5    11    8    15
```

The next row is obtained by working out the differences between numbers next to each other in the first row - we imagine that the last number in the row is next to the first one.

The pattern stops when the numbers are all zero.

Investigate for different sets of starting numbers.

36. GRID DISTANCES

Using points which are on the grid lines, find the distances between them by measuring the shortest route along the grid lines.

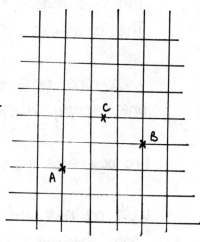

So, in this diagram, distance AB is 4, distance AC is 3·5.

Choose a pair of points. find all points which are the same distance from each of the first two.

Try other problems like this.

37. SIXES

What sums can you find with answer six?

38. LOOPS

This is a node   •

This is an arc   (

With one node and one arc we can make one 'loopy' diagram

(no loose ends are allowed, e.g. like this •—)

With one node and two arcs there are two 'loopy' diagrams:

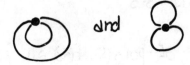

and

What about one node and three arcs?
four arcs?

ten arcs?

Investigate further.
What about <u>two</u> nodes and one arc?

39. CHAINS

$$6 \rightarrow 3 \rightarrow 10 \rightarrow 5 \rightarrow 16 \rightarrow \ldots$$

RULES:
1. If a number is <u>even</u>, divide it by 2
2. If a number is <u>odd</u>, multiply it by 3 and add 1

Continue the chain above. What happens?

Choose other starting numbers and see what happens.
Try to put all your results together on one diagram.

Try changing the rules
e.g. alter Rule 2.
If a number is <u>odd</u>, multiply it by 3 and subtract 1.

40. FLOPPING A RECTANGLE

Start (on squared paper) with a 2 by 1
rectangle with edges labelled a, b, c, d

Flop the rectangle
over edge a; mark
the new position A;
now flop over edge b and mark the new
position AB (A followed
by B) Continue in
this way until you
can label every space.

BC	B	AB
	START	A
		AD

There is more than one route to each
space - eg ABA and B lead to the
same place.

Investigate ways of deciding whether labels
are equivalent.

Investigate the same problem on a triangular
grid.

41. KNIGHT'S TOUR

A knight's tour on a chessboard is made by
moving the knight from square to square
until every square has been visited just once.
If the knight can get back to the starting
square, it is a closed tour.

Investigate the possibility of making knight's
tours on small rectangular boards.

42. NECKLACES

This is a necklace
made of 5 beads,
2 black and three
white. Only one other
different necklace can
be made with these
five beads.

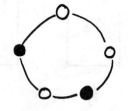

Investigate what different necklaces can
be made with various numbers of black
and white beads.

43. BRAILLE

Louis Braille, a frenchman living in the 19th Century, invented an alphabet for use by blind people.

The alphabet consisted of raised dots in rectangular patterns. Each pattern of dots was based on a 3×2 rectangle.

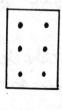

Some patterns used are given below:

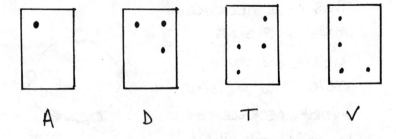

A   D   T   V

How many different patterns can be made using this system?

Investigate for different sized rectangles

44. PASCAL VARIATIONS

In Pascal's triangle, each number is produced by adding the two numbers above:

```
            1
           1 1
          1 2 1
         1 3 3 1
        1 4 6 4 1
```

3   1
  ↘ ↙
   4

Investigate other rules for producing triangles of numbers

45. CONSTRUCTIONS

Investigate constructions which are possible using

a) straight edge and compass
b) straight edge and fixed compass
c) straight edge only
d) straight edge marked with 2 points
e) ruler with 2 parallel straight edges
f) moveable compass only

46. HEXA-PUZZLES

Here are four ways of cutting up a hexagon to make further hexagons, parallelograms, equilateral triangles etc.

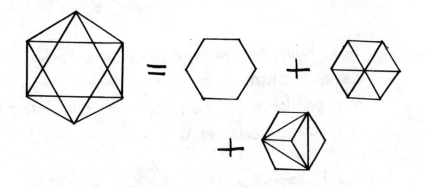

Investigate ways of dissecting hexagons.

47. SQUARE PATTERNS

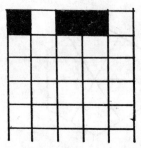

Colour the squares in row 1 with some combination of black and white.

Invent a rule, depending on the colours in the first row, for deciding whether a square in row 2 will be black or white.

Use the same rule to produce row 3 from row 2. Investigate the resulting patterns.

48. BETTING

Investigate bets, say on three teams.
Is it possible to lay bets so that one wins whatever the outcome?
eg Darlington 5 - 4
     Bradford   evens
     Southend   5 - 1

Have the backers covered themselves?

49. PARALLEL AND PERPENDICULAR

Here is a rhombus with its diagonals. The lines are labelled a, b, c, d, e, f

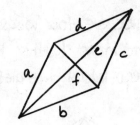

This figure can be represented by an arrow diagram, where $x \rightarrow y$ means x is parallel to y, and $x \dashrightarrow y$ means x is perpendicular to y.

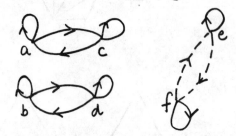

Draw an arrow diagram for a square and its diagonals.

Investigate other arrow diagrams.

50. MAX BOX

Suppose you have a square sheet of card measuring 15 cm by 15 cm and you want to use it to make a box (with out a lid)

You could do this by cutting squares out at the corners and then folding up the sides.

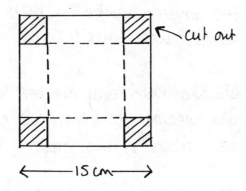

← cut out

←—— 15 cm ——→

Suppose you want the box to have the maximum possible volume.

What size corners would you cut out?

51. MARKS on a RULER

I have a straight edge I want to use as a ruler that will measure any length from 1 cm to 6 cm.
I can do this by putting 7 marks on the straight edge in the usual way, but it can be done with fewer, as each mark can be used for different lengths.
With 3 marks:

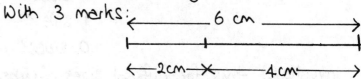

What is the least number of marks I need for all lengths from 1 cm to 6 cm?

Investigate for different lengths.

52. JUGS

If you had a 3-litre jug and a 5-litre jug, how could you use them to measure 4 litres? Investigate other problems like this.

53. PAINTED CUBES

A three by three by three cube is made out of little blocks.

The outside is painted red.
How many little blocks have 3 sides painted?
2 sides?
1 side?
0 sides?
Investigate this for different sizes of cubes.

54. DIVISIBILITY

A test to see if a number is divisible by 3 is to add the digits together and if the answer is divisible by 3, so is the original number.

Find divisibility tests for other numbers.

Find divisibility tests for different bases.

55. CONSECUTIVE SUMS

$$15 = 7 + 8$$
$$9 = 2 + 3 + 4 \quad \text{or} \quad 4 + 5$$
$$10 = 1 + 2 + 3 + 4$$

These three numbers can written as the sum of two or more consecutive integers.

Are there numbers which cannot be written like this?

Starting with any number, say 42, can you decide whether and how it can be written in this way?

Which numbers, like 9 above, can be split up in more than one way?

56. SETS of FIVE

Here is a set of five numbers

$$\{1, 2, 3, 7, 12\}$$

17 can be made by adding some of them together:

$$17 = 12 + 3 + 2$$

Can you make 11? 23? 25?
(You are allowed to use each number only once.)
What is the highest number you can make?
Which numbers can't be made?

Invent other sets of five numbers - try to make a set which produces every number up to the highest.

Extension: Can you make a set of five numbers that will give every number from 1 to 20 but none above 20?

57. DIAGONALS

Investigate the number of squares cut by the diagonal of a rectangle. (In this diagram it is six)

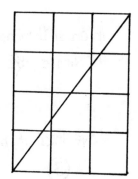

58. FOUR FOURS

What numbers can you make using four 4's and mathematical symbols?

for example

$$\frac{4}{4} + \frac{4}{4} = 2$$

$$4 + 4 + \frac{4}{\sqrt{4}} = 10$$

59. ARITHMOGONS

In an arithmogon, the number in a square must be the sum of the numbers on each side of it:

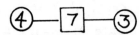

Solve these if possible

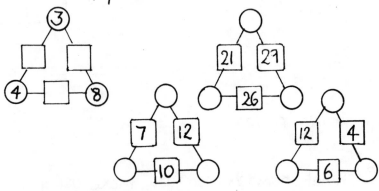

Find a way of solving these (apart from trial and error). Is there always an answer? Only one answer? When are fractions needed? When are negative numbers needed?

Try these

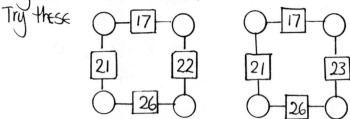

Pentagons? Hexagons?

60. SQUARE NUMBERS

Investigate square numbers in different bases:

BASE

	ten	nine	eight	seven	six	five	four	three	two
S	1	1	1	1	1	1	1	1	1
Q	4	4	4	4	4	4	10	11	100
U	9	10	11	12	13	14	21	100	1001
A	16	17	20	22	24	31	100	121	10000
R	25	27	31	34	41	100	121	221	11001
E	36	40	44	51	100	121	210	1100	100100
S									

61. RAINBOW TRIANGLE

Start from Pascal's triangle. Replace each number with its value in modulo 3 (6 → 0, 11 → 2, 14 → 2) or use one colour for each of 0, 1, 2.

Investigate the patterns that arise.

62. WORMS

Worms leave tracks in layers of mud.

A worm forms a piece of track, turns through 90°, forms another piece, turns, forms another piece, turns, ...

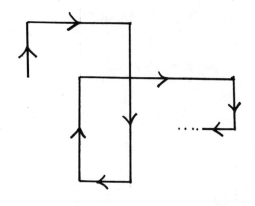

The drawing shows a 1, 2, 3 worm; it makes one unit of track, turns, makes two units of track, turns, makes three units of track, turns, makes one unit of track . . . . .

Investigate worms.

63. PICKING STONES

This is an old Chinese game, for two players. They take it in turns to select stones from two piles, by taking

either: at least one stone from one of the piles (all of them if you like)

or: the same number (at least one) of stones from each pile.

The player who takes all the stones on his turn is the winner.

Investigate for different numbers of stones.

64. CUBE SUMS

Investigate chains of this type

$$57 \rightarrow 5^3 + 7^3 \rightarrow 468 \rightarrow 4^3 + 6^3 + 8^3 \rightarrow$$
$$\text{etc}$$

Any patterns?
Can you generalise from your results?

65. HAPPY NUMBERS

23 is happy!
because

$$23 \nearrow 2^2 \quad 3^2 \searrow$$

$$4 + 9 = 13 \searrow 1^2 \quad 3^2$$

$$1 + 9 = 10 \searrow 1^2 \quad 0^2$$

$$1 + 0 = \boxed{1}$$

If you end up with a 1, the number you started with is happy.

Is 15 happy? What about 7? or 24? Try some others.

How many numbers less than 50 are happy?

Is there a quick way of telling if a number is happy?

Invent a method of producing SAD numbers. Find out which numbers are SAD using your method.

66. POPULATION

In an attempt to stabilise the world population a law has been suggested by a biologist.

This law says that married couples must not produce any more children once they have had a boy.

So families might consist of

B

G B

G G B

G G G B   etc

Is this a good law? that is, will it stabilise the population or not?

Suggest and investigate other laws.

67. SITUATIONS WITH CIRCLES

Two circles can be drawn in one of these ways:

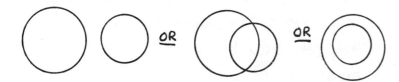

We could place numbers in regions to show the "degree of overlap" as shown below:

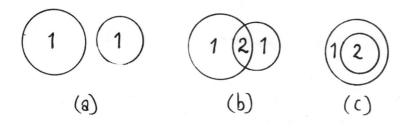

(a)   (b)   (c)

Listing these:

(a) 1, 1

(b) 1, 2, 1

(c) 1, 2

Three circles can be drawn in several ways, one of which is shown below:

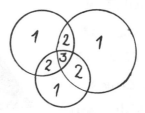

"Degrees of overlap" are shown on the diagram. This situation could be listed as

1, 1, 1, 2, 2, 2, 3.

A simpler situation:

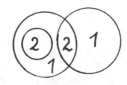

Listed as 1, 1, 2, 2.

There are other possibilities for three circles. How many?
Classify them according to their "degrees of overlap."

68. TRIANGLE DOMINOES

A set of equilateral triangles is produced, each divided as shown. The three sections are coloured with any of 4 colours. A colour may be used more than once in each triangle. The complete set consists of 24 triangles. They are fitted together so that edges touching one another are the same colour. What shapes can be made using all 24 triangles?

69. SQUARING

The fact $a^2 = (a+b)(a-b) + b^2$ can be used to square some numbers mentally.
eg for 77^2, $a = 77$, $b = 3$, $a+b = 80$
so $77^2 = (80 \times 74) + 9 = 5929$.
Investigate for which numbers this would be particularly useful.

70. BOXES

Five equal cubical boxes are arranged in a row. They are so heavy that they can only be tipped about an edge.

A	B	C	D	E

What possible rearrangements of the row can be made?

71. SQUARE BRACKETS

The notation $[\ \ ]$ means "the whole number part of"
eg $[2\cdot7] = 2$, $[5\frac{1}{4}] = 5$, $[6] = 6$

The sequence produced by $[\frac{3}{4}n]$ for $n = 0, 1, 2, \ldots$
is $[0], [\frac{3}{4}], [\frac{6}{4}], [\frac{9}{4}], \ldots$
ie $0, 0, 1, 2, 3, \ldots$
Continue - can you predict what happens?
Investigate $[\frac{a}{b}n]$ - choose your own a, b.

72. CUTTING CORNERS

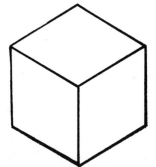

A cube has
6 faces
8 vertices
12 edges

When the corners are cut off, we get
a truncated cube with
? faces
? vertices
? edges.

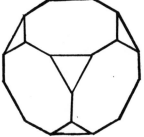

Investigate the effect of truncating some
other simple solid shapes.

73 MOVING TESSELLATIONS

A common tessellation can be transformed in a variety of ways.
One way is to imagine the shapes all moving apart
(outwards). The gaps between the shapes can then be
filled in various ways (depending on how far apart they are,
and how they are oriented relative to each other).

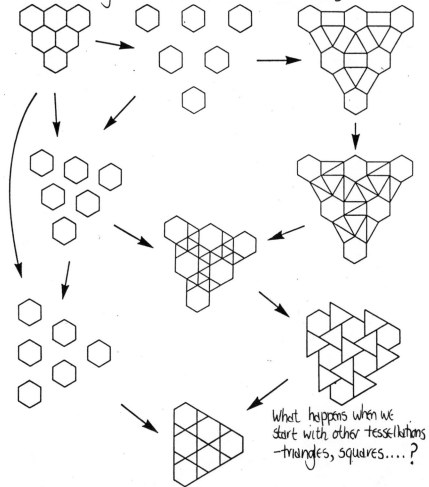

What happens when we
start with other tessellations
—triangles, squares....?

74. CLASSIFYING TESSELLATIONS

This tessellation contains octagons and squares, and three meet at any vertex.

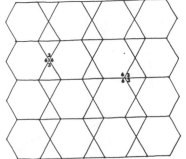

We can describe it as a

$4, \dfrac{8}{3}$ tessellation

Are there any other possible diagrams that fit $4, \dfrac{8}{3}$?
What does a $3, \dfrac{6}{4}$ look like?

Here is one version

More complicated tessellations may have several different kinds of vertex.

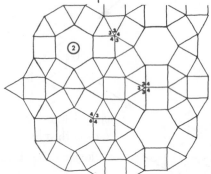

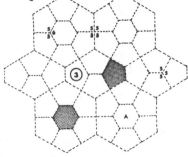

Try to classify known tessellations. Invent descriptions and draw the tessellations to fit them.

75. MAGIC SHAPES

For the magic square you can put the numbers from 1 to 9 in the spaces so that each line adds up to the same total

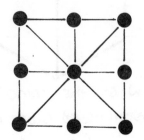

Invent and investigate magic shapes of all kinds. Here are some starters:

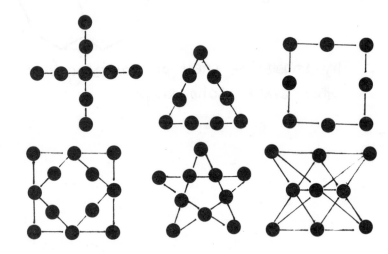